George Catches a Cold

Mummy Pig has said Peppa and George can play in the rain, but they must wear rain clothes to keep them dry.

But George hates wearing his rain hat,
so he has thrown it in a muddy puddle.

Hee, hee!

"Come inside, children," calls Daddy Pig.

"It's raining very hard, now."

"Where's your hat, George?"

asks Mummy Pig.

"Atchoo!" replies George.

Oh dear. George has caught a cold.

"AAAATCHOOOOO!"

George cannot stop sneezing.

"Poor little George," says
Mummy Pig. "You don't look very well."
"Grunt. I'll call Doctor Brown Bear,"
says Daddy Pig.

"Will George go to hospital?" asks Peppa.
"No, George has to go to bed," replies Daddy.
"So George is not properly ill then,"
says Peppa, disappointed.

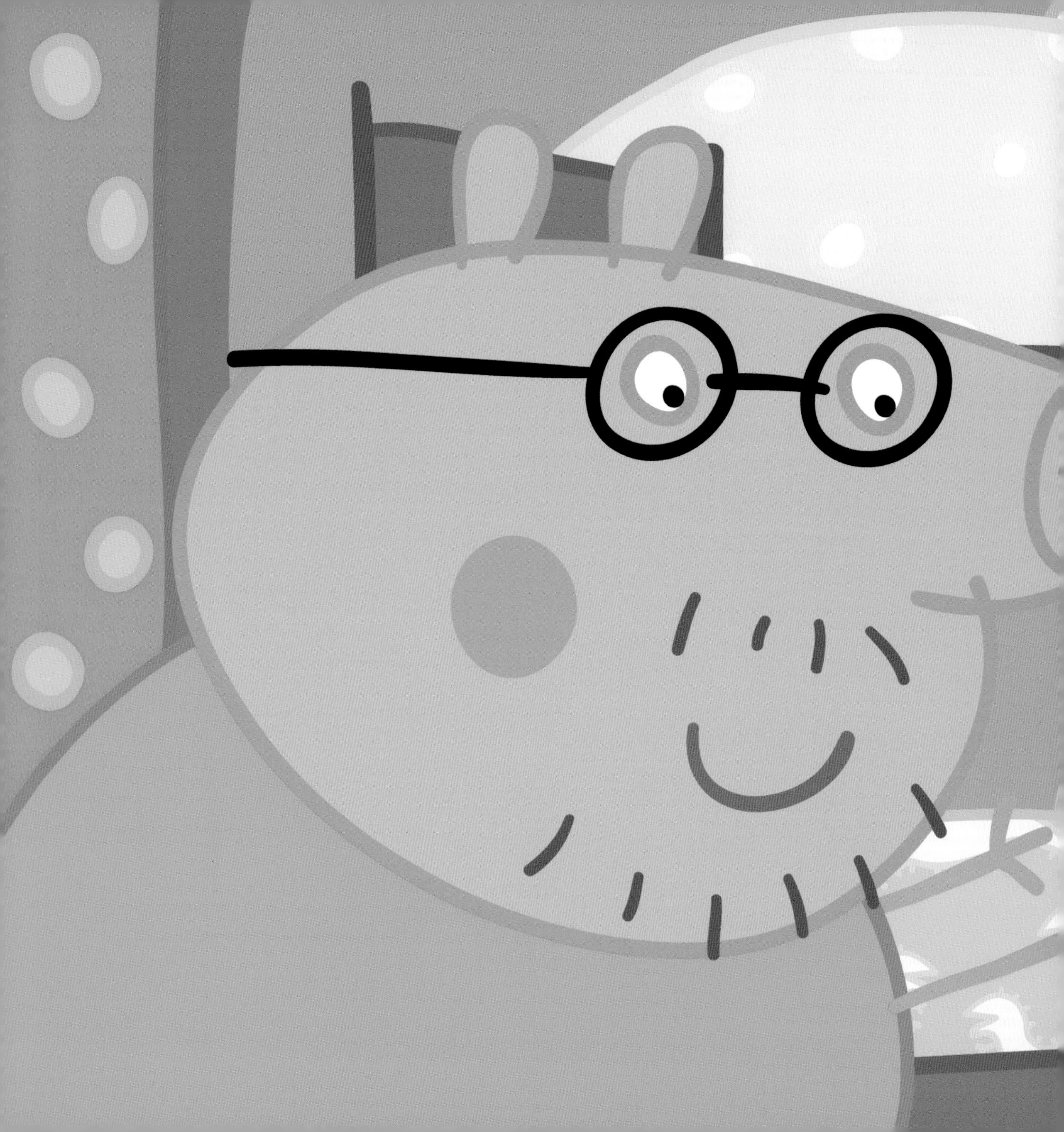

"George, you have to stay in bed until you are better," says Daddy Pig.

"Why?" asks George.

"Because you have to keep warm," says Daddy.

Doctor Brown Bear is here to see George. "Open wide and say 'ahhhh,'" he says. George is a little bit worried. He is hiding under his sheets with Mr Dinosaur.

George finally comes out from under his sheets and opens his mouth wide for Doctor Brown Bear to have a look inside. "Ahhhhhhhh!"

"George has caught a cold," says Doctor
Brown Bear. "He can have some warm
milk at bedtime, to help him sleep."
"Thank you Doctor Brown Bear!" says
Mummy Pig.

"You're welcome. Goodbye!" says
Doctor Brown Bear, before driving off
in his special white car.

The next morning, George wakes up early.
The warm milk made him sleep very well.
"Roar!" cries George. He is feeling much better.

It's a lovely sunny day but George is wearing his rain hat. He doesn't want to catch another cold.

Hee, hee, hee!

"Oh, George!
You don't need to wear your
hat when it is warm and sunny!"
Mummy Pig tells him.

"Hee, hee, hee!" everyone laughs.